Toodle-oodle OOPS!!!

My First School Band Instrument

Bryan Jones

To my family, including my rockstar wife, Cami, who inspires me with her guitar skills (and more) every day, my parents, Jane and Hardy, who encouraged an instrument-fickle kid to stick with music growing up (trombone, sax, bass guitar, guitar, and beyond), and my kids, who impress me so much as they begin their own musical journeys.

Special thanks to France Hernandez, who sprinkles magic on everything she touches (including the cello and electric bass). And many thanks to my review team, who helped improve this book in every way.

Paperback ISBN-13: 978-1-879773-27-1
eBook ISBN-13: 978-1-879773-28-8

D1616620

Music is magical.

It brightens our mood.

Shifting, uplifting,

Our spirits renewed.

Practice makes progress,

Alone and in bands.

Playing, replaying,

Our skill then expands.

Interesting instruments
Bring so many sounds.
Combining, refining,
Pushing the bounds.

Many musical options
To pick from today.
Choosing's confusing,
They're all fun to play.

What are the choices
For school band?
Connecting, selecting,
You'll soon understand.

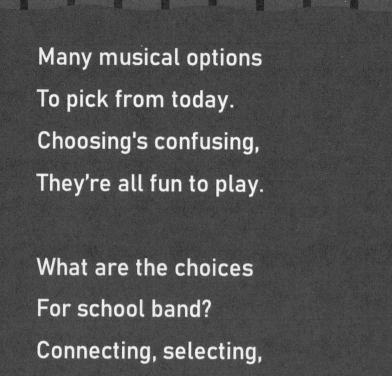

A flutist named Franny

Blows over the hole.

Pressing, caressing,

Keys under control.

 ♫ Toodle-oodle, ♫ **OOPS!!!**

 That's not a song!

 ♫ Toodle-oodle, ♫ **OOPS!!!**

 What's going wrong?

Practice, practice,
Learn your part.

Practice, practice,
That's a good start.

A clarinetist named Chloe
Vibrates the reed.
Blowing and flowing,
Melodic indeed.

♫♫ Doodle, doodle, **SQUAWK!!!**

That's not a song!

♫♫ Doodle, doodle, **SQUAWK!!!**

What's going wrong?

Practice, practice,
Make a plan.

Practice, practice,
You know you can!

A saxophonist named Sammy

Bends all the notes.

Honking and wonking,

A grooving sound floats.

♪ Honky wonk, ♪ BONK!!!

That's not a song!

♪ Honky wonk, ♪ BONK!!!

What's going wrong?

Practice, practice,
Improve your play.

Practice, practice,
Every day.

A trombonist named Tony

Toots the trombone.

Sliding and gliding,

He gets in the zone.

Practice, practice,
Do some drills.

Practice, practice,
Build your skills.

A trumpeter named Trudy

Pushes the keys.

Pressing, depressing,

The valves with ease.

Bub, buuup, **BLURP!!!**

That's not a song!

Bup, buup, **BLURP!!!**

What's going wrong?

Practice, practice,
Don't you stress.

Practice, practice,
Make progress.

Four pals on percussion,

Their rhythm just gels.

Acing the pacing,

Drums, cymbals, and bells.

CRASH! BANG! BOOM!

That's not a song!

CRASH! BANG! BOOM!

What's going wrong?

Practice, practice,
You're coming along.

Practice, practice,
It's almost a song.

A teacher named Tammy
Directs music class.
Conducting, instructing,
The students en masse.

Flute toodle-oodling.

Clarinet doodle det.

Sax honk wonking.

Woodwinds are set!

Trumpet bup buuuping.

Trombone wah wahs.

Blaring, declaring,

The brass has no flaws!

Drums bang-booming.

Winds, brass, percussion,
Together they're stars.
Uniting, delighting,
This music is ours.

We all played together.

Now THAT'S a song!

We all played together.

As one we're strong!

Practice, practice,

We've each learned our part.

Play, play,

Our music is art!

A band can have different instruments.

Brass: Trumpet and trombone are common in early school band. Tubas and French horns are some other brass instruments. School bands, marching bands, jazz bands, and some modern bands include brass.

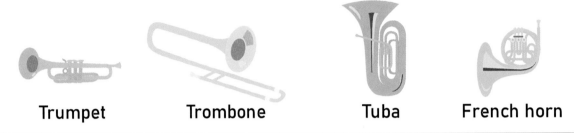

Trumpet   Trombone   Tuba   French horn

Woodwinds: Flute, clarinet, and saxophone are common in early band. Oboes, bassoons, piccolos, and English horns are also woodwinds. School bands, jazz bands, marching bands, orchestras, and some modern bands include woodwinds.

Flute   Bassoon   Oboe

Saxophone   Clarinet

Percussion: Snare and bass drums, bells, and cymbals are common in early school band. Other percussion instruments include drum kits, triangles, cow bells, and more. Most bands include some percussion instruments.

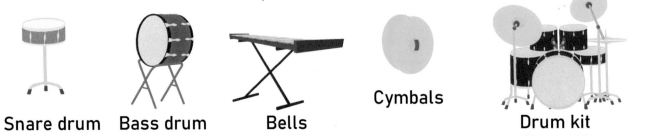

Cymbals

Snare drum   Bass drum   Bells   Drum kit

Of course, there are other instruments, too!

Strings: While not considered school band instruments, strings like violin, cello, and guitar are very popular instruments for children. String bass, viola, and harp are other strings. Orchestra, jazz bands, and modern bands include string instruments.

Guitars   Bass guitar   String bass   Cello   Violin

Keys: While not part of most early school bands, the piano and keyboard are very popular musical instruments for kids. Keys can be acoustic or electric. Jazz bands and modern bands include keys.

Keyboard   Piano

BONUS!

Hear instrument sounds and get bonus Toodle-Oodle-OOPS content online: https://rebrand.ly/oops123

Made in the USA
Coppell, TX
01 June 2022